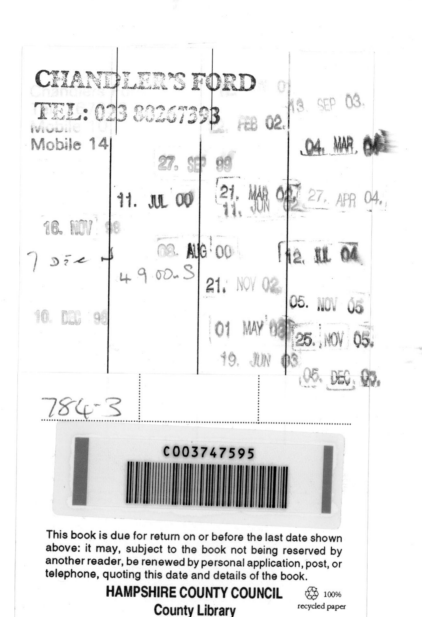

Music for the Millennium The Forties

A Nightingale Sang In Berkeley Square 17
All Or Nothing At All 26
Autumn Leaves (Les Feuilles Mortes) 70
Baby It's Cold Outside 62
Ballerina 57
Besame Mucho 29
Cruising Down The River 54
Ghost Riders In The Sky 66
I'll Remember April 38

Music compiled by Peter Evans and Peter Lavender
Song background notes by Michael Kennedy

All text photographs courtesy of Hulton Getty

Cover photograph of Marlene Dietrich
from The Kobal Collection

Edited by Pearce Marchbank

Text researched and compiled by Heather Page
Book design by Pearce Marchbank and Ben May
Picture research by Nicki Russell

Printed in the United Kingdom by
Page Bros Ltd, Norwich, Norfolk

I'm Beginning To See The Light 48
Long Ago And Far Away 44
So Tired 41
Take Me To Your Heart Again (La Vie En Rose) 50
Take The 'A' Train 35
Tennessee Waltz 60
The Breeze And I 20
The Last Time I Saw Paris 22
There I've Said It Again 32
We'll Meet Again 11
Whispering Grass 14

...clusive Distributors:
...sic Sales Limited
... Frith Street,
...ndon W1V 5TZ, England.
...sic Sales Pty Limited
...) Rothschild Avenue,
...sebery, NSW 2018,
...stralia.

...der No. AM92357
...N 0-7119-4433-4
...s book © Copyright 1997
...Wise Publications

...ur Guarantee of Quality
...publishers, we strive to produce every book
...the highest commercial standards.
...is book has been carefully designed to minimise
...kward page turns and to make playing from
...real pleasure.
...rticular care has been given to specifying acid-free,
...utral-sized paper made from pulps which have not
...en elemental chlorine bleached. This pulp is from
...med sustainable forests and was produced with
...ecial regard for the environment.
...roughout, the printing and binding have been
...nned to ensure a sturdy, attractive publication
...ich should give years of enjoyment.
...our copy fails to meet our high standards,
...ase inform us and we will gladly replace it.

...sic Sales' complete catalogue describes thousands
...titles and is available in full colour sections by
...oject, direct from Music Sales Limited.
...ase state your areas of interest and send a
...eque/postal order for £1.50 for postage to:
...sic Sales Limited, Newmarket Road, Bury St.
...munds, Suffolk IP33 3YB.

...it the Internet Music Shop at
...p://www.musicsales.co.uk

Really, it makes me furious
to think of these ARP people
raking in money like that...
while there are thousands
not knowing where they're
going to get a cup of tea
and a currant bun from
at Christmas.
FROM 'MASS-OBSERVATION'

An air-raid warden sho
regard himself, first a
foremost, as a member of
public, chosen and trair
to be a leader of his fell
citizens and, with them a
for them, do the right thi
in an emergen
HOME OFFICE INSTRUCT

I object to firewatching a
appears to me to be an atten
to prevent the fulfilment of
Scripture which says that
world will be destroyed by fi
MAN OBJECTING TO 1
COMPULSORY ENROLME
IN THE FIRE GUA

At first you think you'll never do it.
You drop your tools and everything.
But the men are very good.
They teach you.
FEMALE RECRUIT TO THE
ROYAL ORDNANCE FACTORIES

Can I do you now sir?
MRS MOPP IN THE BBC
RADIO SHOW 'ITMA'

I sat at home... getting excited abo
this prospect of seeing a real banan
because at that time I'd only seen
them on a film. And eventually she
came in... and revealed this banana
and we both stared at it... it was lik
piece of sculpture, it wasn't a piece
fruit. But my mother, because she'd
seen bananas before the war... says
"You're not eating all that on your
own", and she chopped it in half and
destroyed the whole image of it.
TERRY ALFORD, SCHOOLBOY

Wouldn't get me in one of those things…proper death traps they are in my opinion. A pal of mine has turned his upside down and filled it with water for a duckpond - and that's about the best thing you can do with them.
LONDON SHOPKEEPER ON THE ANDERSON SHELTER

The greatest cross-section of the community came through the centres… let us take the knobbly knees competition, it was nothing weird to see a barrister, doctors and many professional men queuing up with the road sweeper or the refuse person, all getting together and having a very good time.
TED YOUNG, TRAINEE MANAGER AT BUTLIN'S HOLIDAY CAMP, SKEGNESS

German parachute troops, when descending, hold their arms above their heads as if surrendering. The parachutist, however, holds a grenade in each hand.
AIR MINISTRY WARNING

The people were stunned by the news just after the first race at Wolverhampton yesterday but, of course, carried on and presumably the meeting today will go through, if only as a gesture of stoutness.
'DAILY MAIL' RACING CORRESPONDENT ON THE FALL OF FRANCE, MAY, 1940

ore 100 to 30:
gland not out.
WSAGENT'S BOARD DURING
E BATTLE OF BRITAIN

ere is something unreal
out this air war over Britain
You just see a bomber
nting down towards his
rget: three or four things that
ok like marbles fall out, and it
ems to take a long time for
ose bombs to hit the ground
MURROW ON AMERICAN RADIO

I walked down the Mall and stood outside Buckingham Palace, which was floodlit. The crowd was stupendous. The King and Queen came out on the balcony, looking enchanting. We all roared ourselves hoarse. I suppose this is the greatest day in our history.
NOEL COWARD, VE DAY 1945

I have listened attentively to all programmes and nothing will confirm me more in my resolution to emigrate.
EVELYN WAUGH ON THE 'WIRELESS'

AND NOW— WIN THE PEACE

VOTE LABOUR

I don't know what the world is coming to, but I thought I might make some tea.
MRS LANDEMARE, CHURCHILL'S COOK/HOUSEKEEPER, ON HEARING OF HIS DEFEAT IN THE 1945 ELECTION

It was the early edition of the *Evening Standard*, glimpsed over a fellow passenger's shoulder at Oxford Circus, which brought home to my sister Alison and me the full impact of what had happened. There was a picture of our father smiling...and wearing a rosette in his buttonhole and a banner headline 'The New Prime Minister'. Alison and I joined hands and danced our way down Oxford Street.
FELICITY ATTLEE ON HER FATHER'S SUCCESS IN THE 1945 ELECTION

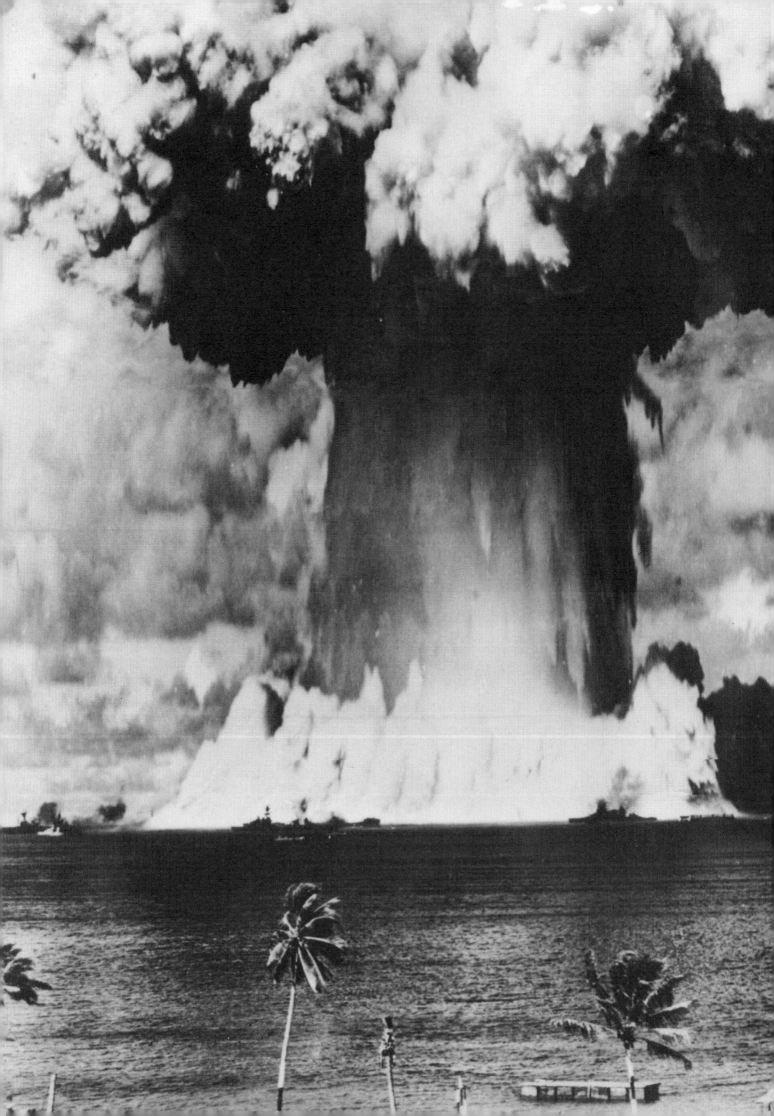

The 1944 Education Act taught me to read and think. The National Health Service has given me nice teeth and the BBC gave me Shakespeare and Beethoven.
GILLIAN REYNOLDS, SPEAKING IN 1989

Mothers used to ring me up and say they were extremely worried, their daughters had expressed the intention of coming to my club … I used to say, "Well, the only thing you're going to get hung up on in 100 Oxford Street is Tizer."
HUMPHREY LYTTELTON, JAZZ MUSICIAN

We are revolutionaries who have not swept anything away. We are a dreary self-righteous people with a passion for gin, tobacco, gambling and ballet. We are a nation of Sabbath keepers who do not go to church. We toil to keep ourselves alive, with three tea-breaks, a five-day week and Wednesday afternoon for the match. We spend so much time arguing about food we have no time to cook it properly. We spend fourpence on our culture, and several million pounds a year advertising it. We get free spectacles and false teeth and, for lack of hospital beds, may die in a ditch. We have probably the best children and the dullest adults in Europe.
PRIESTLEY IN THE 'NEW STATESMAN', 1949

We'll Meet Again

Words & Music by Ross Parker & Hughie Charles.

Ross Parker and Hughie Charles' creative burst of activity in 1939 included one of the classic wartime hits 'We'll Meet Again' that was to become the theme song of the Force's Sweetheart, Vera Lynn, revived so memorably by Dame Vera herself during the televised VE Day commemorative celebrations in 1995.

Lyrics:

Let's say good-bye with a smile dear, just for a while dear, we must part,
don't let the part-ing up-set you, I'll not for-get you sweet-heart.

Af-ter the rain comes the rain-bow, you'll see the rain go, ne-ver fear,
we two can wait for to-mor-row, good-bye to sor-row my dear.

CHORUS

We'll meet a-gain, don't know

I won't be long,_____ they'll be hap-py to know_ that as you saw me go,_ I was sing-ing this song. We'll meet a-gain, don't know where, don't know when, but I know we'll meet a-gain some sun-ny day.

day.

day._____

Whispering Grass

Words by Fred Fisher.
Music by Doris Fisher.

Forever associated with The Inkspots who had a hit with the song in 1941, 'Whispering Grass' enjoyed a fresh lease of life in 1975 when two popular characters from the television comedy series It Ain't Half Hot Mum took it to No. 1 for three weeks. They were 'Lofty', the diminutive Don Estelle, and the Sergeant-Major, played by Windsor Davies.

A Nightingale Sang In Berkeley Square

Words by Eric Maschwitz. Music by Manning Sherwin.

One of the most poignantly evocative of all songs about London, 'A Nightingale Sang In Berkeley Square' was introduced, in wartime, in the London musical revue New Faces by the elegant Judy Campbell. Sadly, she was not asked to record it. However, many others did - with great success, including Frank Sinatra and Tony Bennett.

The Breeze And I

Words by Al Stillman.
Music by Ernesto Lecuona.

Cuban composer Ernesto Lecuona wrote many distinguished classical compositions. In 1940, United States music publishers took an interest in Latin American music and Lecuona was one of the beneficiaries. His piano composition 'Andalucia' formed the basis for the popular song 'The Breeze And I' with English words by Al Stillman.

In 1940 Oscar Hammerstein saw with intense sorrow the collapse of the French forces against the might of the German Reich. He wrote the words and Jerome Kern the melody to 'The Last Time I Saw Paris', subsequently featured in many motion pictures, including Lady Be Good and Till the Clouds Roll By. The song won an Academy Award in 1941.

The Last Time I Saw Paris

Music by Jerome Kern.
Words by Oscar Hammerstein II.

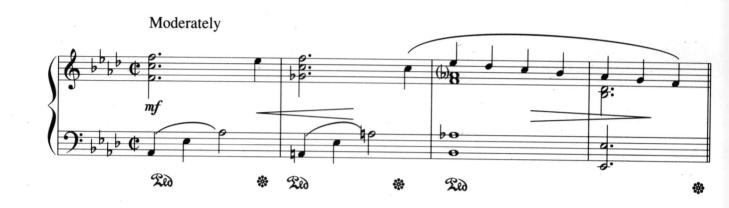

The last time I saw Par - is her heart was warm and

gay; I heard the laugh - ter of her heart in

ev' - ry street ca - fé. The last time I saw

Par - is, her trees were dressed for spring, and

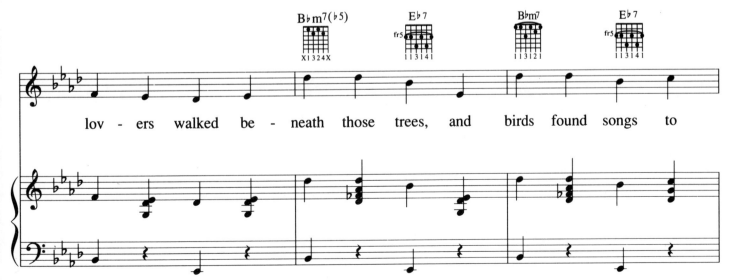

lov - ers walked be - neath those trees, and birds found songs to

sing.   I dodged the same old tax - i cabs that

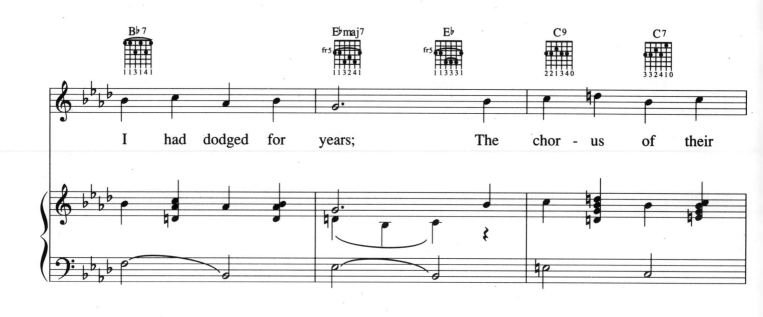

I had dodged for years;   The chor - us of their

squeak - y horns was mu - sic to my ears.   The last time I saw

All Or Nothing At All

Words & Music by Arthur Altman & Jack Lawrence.

Besame Mucho

English Words by Sunny Skylar.
Music by Consuelo Velazquez.

The Forties saw a sudden explosion of music from Latin America on to the popular music scene. 'Besame Mucho', a song from Mexico with music by Consuelo Velazquez, gained English lyrics by Sunny Skylar and became a hit in the 1944 film Follow The Boys and also in Club Havana. In 1995 Clarke Peters included the song in his Nat 'King' Cole show Unforgettable.

Hold me my dar-ling and say that you'll al-ways be mine. _____
que ten-go mie-do per-der-te, per-der-te o-tra vez. _____

This joy is some-thing new, My arms en-fold-ing you, Nev-er knew this thrill be-
Quie-ro te-ner-te muy cer-ca, mi-rar-me en tus o-jos, ver-te jun-to a

fore, Who ev-er thought I'd be hold-ing you close to me,
mí, pien-sa que tal vez ma-ña-na yo ya es-ta-ré

Whisp-'ring "It's you I a-dore." Dear-est one, _____ If you should
le-jos, muy le-jos de ti. Bé-sa-me, _____ Bé-sa-me

There I've Said It Again

Words & Music by Redd Evans & Dave Mann.

Redd Evans and Dave Mann collaborated on a number of all-time standards, including 'No Moon At All,' and 'Don't Go To Strangers'. 'There I've Said It Again' was an immediate success, again in 1945 and subsequently in 1947 and 1964. Classic recordings feature Jimmy Young, Vaughn Monroe, Nat 'King' Cole and The Four Aces.

Lyrics:

I think I've talked too much already, ___ yet the words con-tin-ue to flow. And when I place them all to-geth-er ___ they still seem to say "I love you so," ___ I've said it. ___ What

Take The 'A' Train

Words & Music by Billy Strayhorn

Billy Strayhorn, who was for so long Duke Ellington's pianist and arranger, composed Ellington's theme tune 'Take The 'A' Train'. It was featured in the film Reveille with Beverly in 1943, and used in the successful stage shows Bubbling Brown Sugar and Sophisticated Ladies. The 'A' Train is one of New York's subway trains that passes through Harlem.

Medium beat

If you want to go to Har-lem, 'way up to Su-gar Hill,___ where those danc-ing feet you read of are ne-ver, ne-ver still. Then you_____ must take the 'A' train_____

I'll Remember April

Words & Music by Don Raye, Gene de Paul & Patricia Johnson.

Bud Abbott and Lou Costello played hot dog sellers on a dude ranch in the comedy film musical Ride 'Em Cowboy. Don Raye and Gene de Paul contributed some memorable songs, and Ella Fitzgerald was around to sing them. 'I'll Remember April' was the big hit - and even inspired a further film bearing the song's title.

So Tired

Words & Music by Russ Morgan & Jack Stuart.

Although memorable versions were recorded later on by Frankie Vaughan and Kay Starr, the original, definitive recording of 'So Tired' was by its bandleader/composer Russ Morgan, who wrote it with Jack Stuart, and recorded the song himself. It became Russ Morgan's signature tune.

When night is fall - ing I feel so lone - ly, my heart is call - ing, I need you on - ly. I'm so tired of wait - ing for you, so tired

all day long I won-der why we're far a-part.—

So tired of dream-ing of you, so tired

of wait-ing for you, but tho' I'm tir-ed I'll wait for-ev-er

dear._____ I'm dear._____

Long Ago And Far Away

Music by Jerome Kern.
Words by Ira Gershwin.

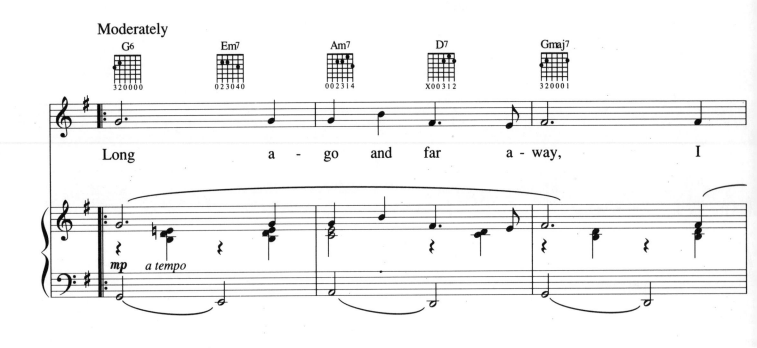

Long a - go and far a - way, I

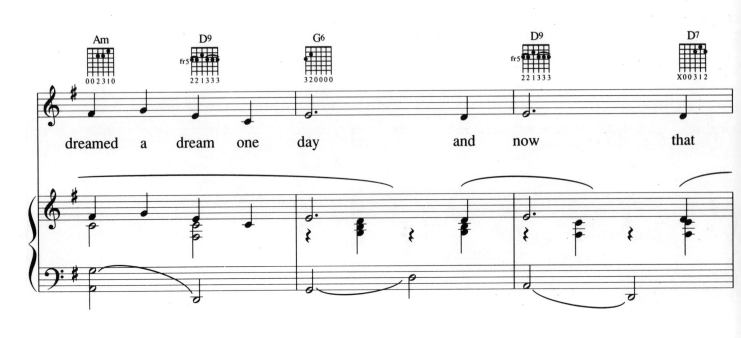

dreamed a dream one day and now that

Just one look and then I knew_____ _____ that all I longed for long a-go was

1. you.

2. you._____ _____

Here's a song partly written by three of the greatest names in 40's swing - bandleaders Harry James, Duke Ellington and saxophone genius Johnny Hodges with Don George - the latter's credits also include 'The Yellow Rose Of Texas'. The song was featured in the film The Man From Oklahoma.

I'm Beginning To See The Light

Words & Music by Harry James, Duke Ellington,
Johnny Hodges & Don George.

now when you turn the lamp down low__ I'm Be - gin - ning To See The Light____

Used to ram - ble thru the park ___ Shad - ow box - ing in the dark ___

Then you came and caused a spark,__ That's a four a - larm fire__ now_____ I

nev - er made love by lan - tern shine,__ I nev - er saw rain - bows in my wine,__ But

now that your lips are burn - ing mine,__ I'm Be - gin - ning To See The Light___ I____

8vb

49

Take Me To Your Heart Again
(La Vie En Rose)

Music by R. S. Louiguy.
English Lyric by Frank Eyton.

ev - er may be - fall, _____ Life is short, and love is

all. _____ Take me to your heart a - gain, Let's

make a start a - gain, For - giv - ing and for - get -

-ting; Take me to your heart a - gain, And

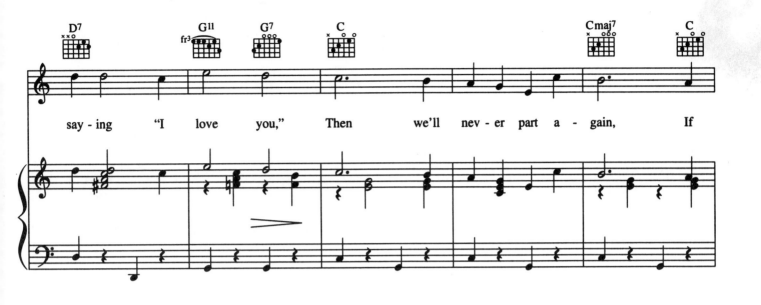

say - ing "I love you," Then we'll nev - er part a - gain, If

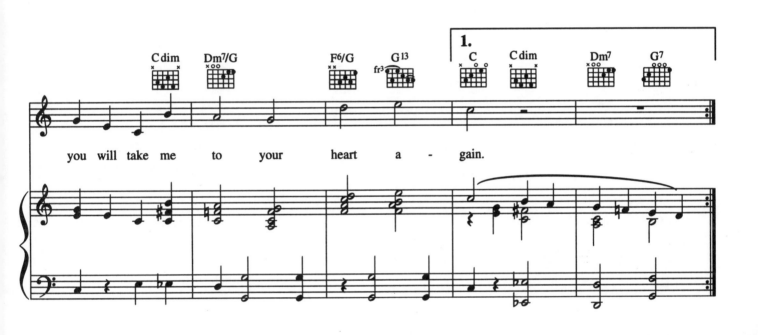

you will take me to your heart a - gain.

1.

2.

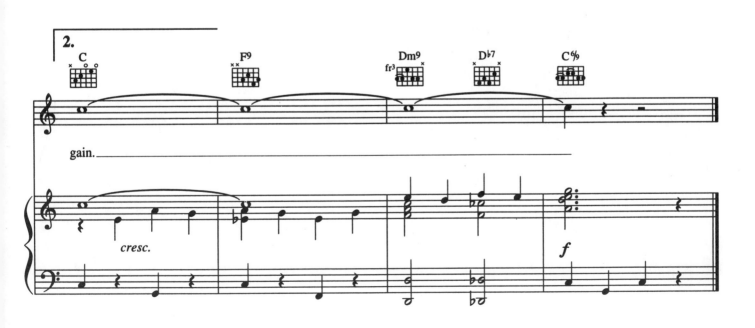

gain.

cresc.

f

Cruising Down The River

Words & Music by Eily Beadell & Nell Tollerton.

The winning entry in a 1945 songwriting contest, 'Cruising Down The River' was the work of two English writers who were never again to enjoy such success. The song proved so popular abroad that in 1953 Columbia Pictures starred Dick Haymes in a musical about a singer who inherits a riverboat. Its title? Cruising Down The River.

Ballerina

Music by Carl Sigman.
Words by Bob Russell.

Vaughn Monroe and Bing Crosby both had hits with Carl Sigman and Bob Russell's 'Ballerina', a 1947 ballad by two experienced writers who individually would continue to create hits for decades to come - Sigman with 'Ebb Tide', 'Answer Me' and 'What Now My Love?' and Bob Russell with 'Little Green Apples' and 'He Ain't Heavy...He's My Brother'.

Moderato

1. Dance Bal - le - ri - na dance and do your pir - ou - ette in rhy - thm with your ach - ing heart.
2. Whirl Bal - le - ri - na whirl and just ig - nore the chair that's emp - ty in the sec - ond row.

Dance bal - le - ri - na dance you must - n't once for -
This is your mo - ment girl al - though he's not out

get   a   danc-er has   to dance the   part.____

there   ap-plaud-ing as   you   steal   the   show.____

Tacet

Once you said____   his love must wait   its   turn.____

____ You want-ed fame in - stead____   I guess that's your con - cern____ we live and

learn.____ And love is   gone, Bal-le-ri - na,   gone.   So on with your ca -

Tennessee Waltz

Words & Music by Redd Stewart & Pee Wee King.

Country legends Redd Stewart and Pee Wee King wrote 'Tennessee Waltz ' in the Forties, but it really hit the spot in the early 1950s, reaching No.1 position in sheet music sales in 1951. Successful recordings included versions by Teddy Johnson, Petula Clark, Jo Stafford, Patti Page and an irreverent version by Spike Jones.

CHORUS

I was waltz-ing___ with my dar-lin'___ to the Ten-nes - see___ Waltz___ When an old friend I hap-pened to see___ In-tro-duced him___ to my loved one___ and___ while they___ were___ waltz-ing My

Baby It's Cold Outside

Words & Music by Frank Loesser.

By 1946, lyricist Frank Loesser was also writing his own music. For Neptune's Daughter, he came up with a cute novelty number for swimming star Esther Williams and Ricardo Montalban as her South American romantic interest. The song deservedly won the Academy Award for best film song for 1948.

Loesserando

F9

nice _____ My moth-er will start to wor-ry _____ And
warm _____ My sis-ter will be sus-pi-cious _____ My

I'll hold your hands _____ They're just like ice.
Look out the win-dow at that storm

Bb6

Beau-ti-ful, what's your
Gosh, your lips look de -

Bb9

fath-er will be pac-ing the floor
broth-er will be there at the door

hur-ry? _____ Lis-ten to the fi-re-place roar!
li-cious _____ Waves up-on a trop-i-cal shore!

F6

So real-ly I'd bet-ter
My maid-en aunt's mind is

scur-ry. _____ Well, may-be just a half a drink more
vi-cious _____ Well, may-be just a ci-ga-rette more

Gm7

Beau-ti-ful, please, don't hur-ry _____
Gosh, your lips are de-li-cious _____

C7

The
I've

Put some re-cords on while I pour _____
Nev-er such a bliz-zard be-fore _____

64

65

Ghost Riders In The Sky

Words & Music by Stan Jones.

Briskly

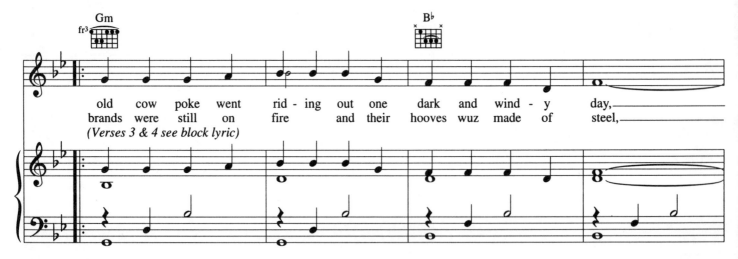

old cow poke went rid- ing out one dark and wind- y day,
brands were still on fire and their hooves wuz made of steel,
(Verses 3 & 4 see block lyric)

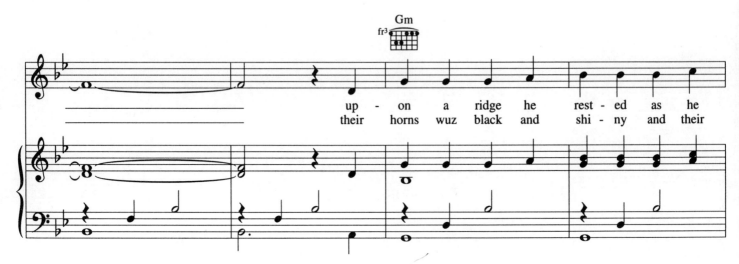

up- on a ridge he rest- ed as he
their horns wuz black and shi- ny and their

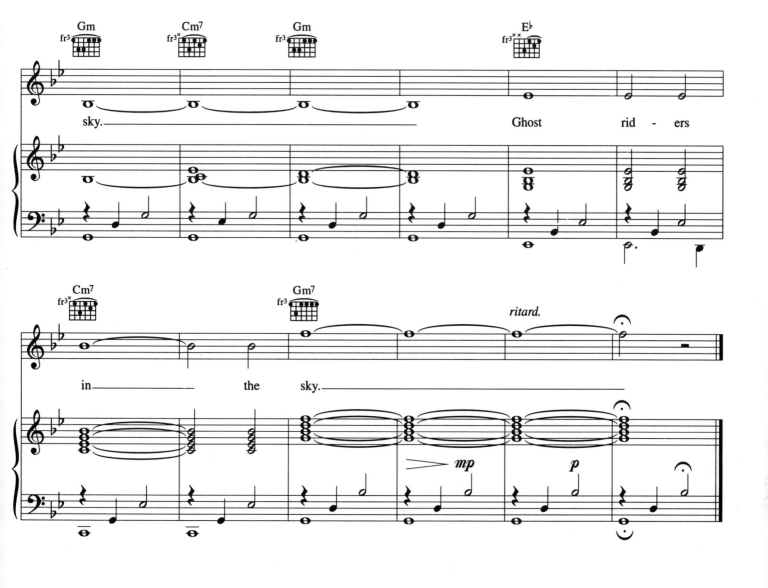

Verse 3:

Their faces gaunt their eyes were blurred and shirts all soaked with sweat,
They're ridin' hard to catch that herd but they ain't caught them yet,
'Cause they've got to ride forever on that range up in the sky
On horses snortin' fire as they ride on, hear their cry.
Yi-pi-yi-ay, yi-pi-yi-o, the ghost riders in the sky.

Verse 4:

As the riders loped on by him he heard one call his name,
"If you want to save your soul from hell a ridin' on our range.
Then cowboy change your ways today or with us you will ride
A-try'n to catch the devil's herd across these endless skies."
Yi-pi-yi-ay, yi-pi-yi-o, the ghost herd in the sky.
Ghost riders in the sky.

Autumn Leaves
(Les Feuilles Mortes)

Music by Joseph Kosma. Words by Jacques Prevert.
English Lyrics by Johnny Mercer

Johnny Mercer provided the English lyrics for one of the great romantic ballads from France - 'Les Feuilles Mortes'. Jacques Prevert, author of the original words, was one of France's greatest poets of the 30s and 40s. Joseph Kosma wrote countless film scores and popular songs - but none as popular as 'Autumn Leaves'.

Slowly, with much feeling

The fall - ing leaves _____ drift by my win - dow, _____ the au - tumn leaves _____ of red and gold. I see your lips, _____ the sum - mer kiss - es, _____ the sun - burned hands _____ I used to hold. Since you

tous, _____ les deux en - sem - ble. _____ Toi qui m'ai - mais _____ moi qui t'ai -

mais. Mais la vie sé - pare _____ ceax qui s'ai - ment _____ tout dou - ce -

ment _____ sans faire de bruit. Et la mer ef - fa - ce sur le

sa - ble les pas des a - mants dé - su - nis.